CW00343033

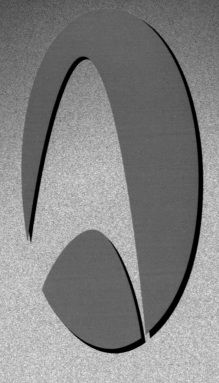

THE
1996
STAR TREK®
DIARY

Space - the final frontier.

These are the voyages of the Starship Enterprise™.

Its ongoing mission: to explore strange new worlds, to seek out new lifeforms and new civilisations...

To boldly go where no-one has gone before.

THE 1996 STAR TREK® DIARY

POCKET
BOOKS

1996/1997 CALENDARS

1996

JANUARY
M	T	W	T	F	S	S
1	2	3	4	5	6	7
8	9	10	11	12	13	14
15	16	17	18	19	20	21
22	23	24	25	26	27	28
29	30	31				

FEBRUARY
M	T	W	T	F	S	S
			1	2	3	4
5	6	7	8	9	10	11
12	13	14	15	16	17	18
19	20	21	22	23	24	25
26	27	28	29			

MARCH
M	T	W	T	F	S	S
				1	2	3
4	5	6	7	8	9	10
11	12	13	14	15	16	17
18	19	20	21	22	23	24
25	26	27	28	29	30	31

APRIL
M	T	W	T	F	S	S
1	2	3	4	5	6	7
8	9	10	11	12	13	14
15	16	17	18	19	20	21
22	23	24	25	26	27	28
29	30					

MAY
M	T	W	T	F	S	S
		1	2	3	4	5
6	7	8	9	10	11	12
13	14	15	16	17	18	19
20	21	22	23	24	25	26
27	28	29	30	31		

JUNE
M	T	W	T	F	S	S
					1	2
3	4	5	6	7	8	9
10	11	12	13	14	15	16
17	18	19	20	21	22	23
24	25	26	27	28	29	30

JULY
M	T	W	T	F	S	S
1	2	3	4	5	6	7
8	9	10	11	12	13	14
15	16	17	18	19	20	21
22	23	24	25	26	27	28
29	30	31				

AUGUST
M	T	W	T	F	S	S
			1	2	3	4
5	6	7	8	9	10	11
12	13	14	15	16	17	18
19	20	21	22	23	24	25
26	27	28	29	30	31	

SEPTEMBER
M	T	W	T	F	S	S
30						1
2	3	4	5	6	7	8
9	10	11	12	13	14	15
16	17	18	19	20	21	22
23	24	25	26	27	28	29

OCTOBER
M	T	W	T	F	S	S
	1	2	3	4	5	6
7	8	9	10	11	12	13
14	15	16	17	18	19	20
21	22	23	24	25	26	27
28	29	30	31			

NOVEMBER
M	T	W	T	F	S	S
				1	2	3
4	5	6	7	8	9	10
11	12	13	14	15	16	17
18	19	20	21	22	23	24
25	26	27	28	29	30	

DECEMBER
M	T	W	T	F	S	S
30	31					1
2	3	4	5	6	7	8
9	10	11	12	13	14	15
16	17	18	19	20	21	22
23	24	25	26	27	28	29

1997

JANUARY
M	T	W	T	F	S	S
		1	2	3	4	5
6	7	8	9	10	11	12
13	14	15	16	17	18	19
20	21	22	23	24	25	26
27	28	29	30	31		

FEBRUARY
M	T	W	T	F	S	S
					1	2
3	4	5	6	7	8	9
10	11	12	13	14	15	16
17	18	19	20	21	22	23
24	25	26	27	28		

MARCH
M	T	W	T	F	S	S
31					1	2
3	4	5	6	7	8	9
10	11	12	13	14	15	16
17	18	19	20	21	22	23
24	25	26	27	28	29	30

APRIL
M	T	W	T	F	S	S
	1	2	3	4	5	6
7	8	9	10	11	12	13
14	15	16	17	18	19	20
21	22	23	24	25	26	27
28	29	30				

MAY
M	T	W	T	F	S	S
			1	2	3	4
5	6	7	8	9	10	11
12	13	14	15	16	17	18
19	20	21	22	23	24	25
26	27	28	29	30	31	

JUNE
M	T	W	T	F	S	S
30						1
2	3	4	5	6	7	8
9	10	11	12	13	14	15
16	17	18	19	20	21	22
23	24	25	26	27	28	29

JULY
M	T	W	T	F	S	S
	1	2	3	4	5	6
7	8	9	10	11	12	13
14	15	16	17	18	19	20
21	22	23	24	25	26	27
28	29	30	31			

AUGUST
M	T	W	T	F	S	S
				1	2	3
4	5	6	7	8	9	10
11	12	13	14	15	16	17
18	19	20	21	22	23	24
25	26	27	28	29	30	31

SEPTEMBER
M	T	W	T	F	S	S
1	2	3	4	5	6	7
8	9	10	11	12	13	14
15	16	17	18	19	20	21
22	23	24	25	26	27	28
29	30					

OCTOBER
M	T	W	T	F	S	S
		1	2	3	4	5
6	7	8	9	10	11	12
13	14	15	16	17	18	19
20	21	22	23	24	25	26
27	28	29	30	31		

NOVEMBER
M	T	W	T	F	S	S
					1	2
3	4	5	6	7	8	9
10	11	12	13	14	15	16
17	18	19	20	21	22	23
24	25	26	27	28	29	30

DECEMBER
M	T	W	T	F	S	S
1	2	3	4	5	6	7
8	9	10	11	12	13	14
15	16	17	18	19	20	21
22	23	24	25	26	27	28
29	30	31				

◖ CREW MANIFEST

Name _____

Home Planet Address _____

_____ Coordinates _____

Crew Number _____ Fax _____

Starfleet Rank _____ Starship _____

Chief Medical Officer _____

Chief Dental Officer _____

Emergency Contact at Starfleet Command _____

Shuttlecraft Insurance Policy Number _____

Shuttlecraft Insurance Due _____

Galactic Space Service Number _____

MOST FREQUENT COORDINATES

Name	Coordinates
_____	_____
_____	_____
_____	_____
_____	_____
_____	_____
_____	_____
_____	_____

616 784
891 884
241 681
337 987
854 254
994 **774**
824 321

IMPORTANT STARDATES

Stardate	Stardate
_____	_____
_____	_____
_____	_____
_____	_____
_____	_____
_____	_____

616
891
241
337
854
994

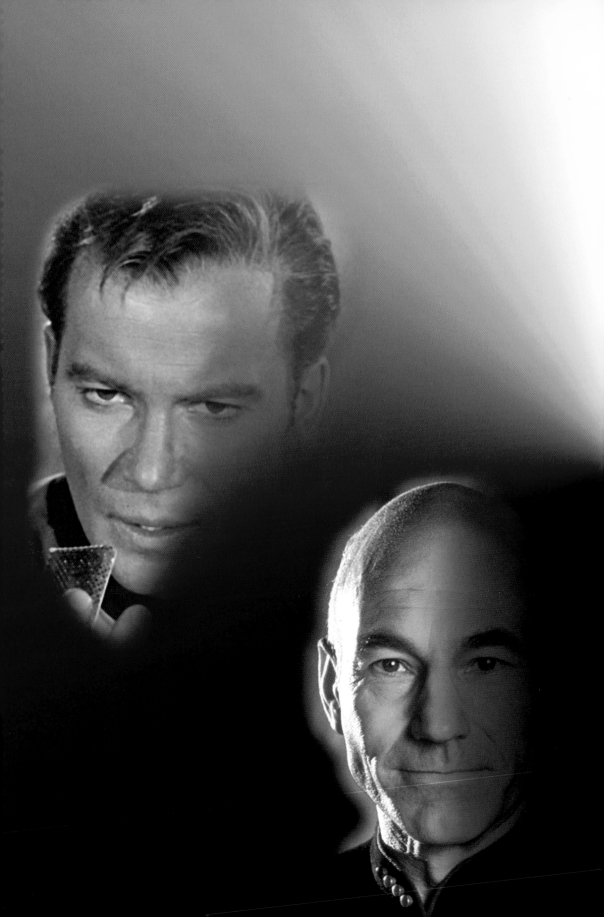

10045

10046

10047

Gene Roddenberry created STAR TREK® with the innovative pilot *The Cage*. Jeffrey Hunter portrayed Captain Christopher Pike, a fine captain but one troubled with the weight of command.

Mr Spock was also featured in the pilot, which was ground-breaking in that it was the most expensive TV pilot ever produced, and it had a female second in command, "Number One" played by Majel Barrett. ∎

10048

DECEMBER						1995
M	T	W	T	F	S	S
				1	2	3
4	5	6	7	8	9	10
11	12	13	14	15	16	17
18	19	20	21	22	23	24
25	26	27	28	29	30	31

JANUARY						1996
M	T	W	T	F	S	S
1	2	3	4	5	6	7
8	9	10	11	12	13	14
15	16	17	18	19	20	21
22	23	24	25	26	27	28
29	30	31				

FEBRUARY						1996
M	T	W	T	F	S	S
			1	2	3	4
5	6	7	8	9	10	11
12	13	14	15	16	17	18
19	20	21	22	23	24	25
26	27	28	29			

◀ JANUARY ▬▬

New Year's Day

MONDAY **1**

Brent Spiner's Birthday (Lieutenant Commander Data)

Bank Holiday (Scotland)
New Year's Holiday (New Zealand)

TUESDAY **2**

WEDNESDAY **3**

THURSDAY **4**

FRIDAY **5**

Epiphany (Germany)
Three Kings' Day (Spain)

SATURDAY **6**

SUNDAY **7**

CAPTAIN JAMES T. KIRK

616 784
891 884
241 681
337 987
854 254
994 **774**
824 321

Bold Captain of the *U.S.S. Enterprise*™, James T Kirk embodies strength and the utmost ability to lead his crew of 432 into the risky business of space exploration.

    A captain who leads by example, Kirk protects his ship and his crew at all times. This unswerving devotion to duty has provided him with a crew that is painstakingly loyal and a credit to the Federation. ■

784
884
681
987
254
774
321

DECEMBER						1995
M	T	W	T	F	S	S
				1	2	3
4	5	6	7	8	9	10
11	12	13	14	15	16	17
18	19	20	21	22	23	24
25	26	27	28	29	30	31

JANUARY						1996
M	T	W	T	F	S	S
1	2	3	4	5	6	7
8	9	10	11	12	13	14
15	16	17	18	19	20	21
22	23	24	25	26	27	28
29	30	31				

FEBRUARY						1996
M	T	W	T	F	S	S
			1	2	3	4
5	6	7	8	9	10	11
12	13	14	15	16	17	18
19	20	21	22	23	24	25
26	27	28	29			

JANUARY

MONDAY 8

TUESDAY 9

WEDNESDAY 10

THURSDAY 11

The original U.S.S. Enterprise™ *NCC-1701*

FRIDAY 12

SATURDAY 13

SUNDAY 14

THE FIRST OFFICER

Captain Kirk's first officer and close friend is the half-Vulcan, half-human Mr Spock. He has the perfect credentials to be an excellent science officer and second-in-command. Enigmatic and unswervingly loyal, Spock always provides the logical point of view to any problem encountered. ∎

DECEMBER						1995		JANUARY						1996		FEBRUARY						1996
M	T	W	T	F	S	S		M	T	W	T	F	S	S		M	T	W	T	F	S	S
				1	2	3		1	2	3	4	5	6	7					1	2	3	4
4	5	6	7	8	9	10		8	9	10	11	12	13	14		5	6	7	8	9	10	11
11	12	13	14	15	16	17		15	16	17	18	19	20	21		12	13	14	15	16	17	18
18	19	20	21	22	23	24		22	23	24	25	26	27	28		19	20	21	22	23	24	25
25	26	27	28	29	30	31		29	30	31						26	27	28	29			

JANUARY

Martin Luther King Jr Birthday (USA)

MONDAY 15

LeVar Burton's Birthday (Lieutenant Commander Geordi La Forge)

TUESDAY 16

WEDNESDAY 17

THURSDAY 18

FRIDAY 19

DeForest Kelley's Birthday (Dr Leonard "Bones" McCoy)

SATURDAY 20

SUNDAY 21

ENTERPRISING CREW

Many people make up the crew of the *U.S.S. Enterprise*™. Dr Leonard 'Bones' McCoy is the chief medical officer. A passionate character, he has an impulsive approach to problems.

Janice Rand is the captain's yeoman, and her duty is to assist the captain. In the episode *Miri,* however, it is Captain Kirk who helps her, giving her the strength to carry on when the landing party is infected with a deadly virus. ∎

DECEMBER						1995		JANUARY						1996		FEBRUARY						1996
M	T	W	T	F	S	S		M	T	W	T	F	S	S		M	T	W	T	F	S	S
				1	2	3		1	2	3	4	5	6	7					1	2	3	4
4	5	6	7	8	9	10		8	9	10	11	12	13	14		5	6	7	8	9	10	11
11	12	13	14	15	16	17		15	16	17	18	19	20	21		12	13	14	15	16	17	18
18	19	20	21	22	23	24		22	23	24	25	26	27	28		19	20	21	22	23	24	25
25	26	27	28	29	30	31		29	30	31						26	27	28	29			

JANUARY

MONDAY **22**

TUESDAY **23**

WEDNESDAY **24**

THURSDAY **25**

Australia Day (Australia)

FRIDAY **26**

SATURDAY **27**

SUNDAY **28**

The most dangerous part of space exploration is when a landing party is required to investigate an alien landscape. Here the crew are under pressure to monitor their equipment and to avoid confrontations.

In the episodes *Menagerie, Part I* and *II*, Kirk is affronted when Spock commandeers the *U.S.S. Enterprise*™ without authority, to improve Captain Pike's quality of life. The episode (the only two-part episode of the original series) guest stars Malachi Throne who, coincidentally, also guest stars in the STAR TREK®: THE NEXT GENERATION™ two-part episode, *Unification.* ∎

77453284
66224482

616 784
891 884
241 681
337 987
854 254
994 **774**
824 321

DECEMBER						1995
M	T	W	T	F	S	S
				1	2	3
4	5	6	7	8	9	10
11	12	13	14	15	16	17
18	19	20	21	22	23	24
25	26	27	28	29	30	31

JANUARY						1996
M	T	W	T	F	S	S
1	2	3	4	5	6	7
8	9	10	11	12	13	14
15	16	17	18	19	20	21
22	23	24	25	26	27	28
29	30	31				

FEBRUARY						1996
M	T	W	T	F	S	S
			1	2	3	4
5	6	7	8	9	10	11
12	13	14	15	16	17	18
19	20	21	22	23	24	25
26	27	28	29			

◀ JANUARY-FEBRUARY ■

MONDAY 29

Leonard Nimoy as the alternative universe Spock in Mirror Mirror

TUESDAY 30

WEDNESDAY 31

THURSDAY 1

FRIDAY 2

SATURDAY 3

SUNDAY 4

In *Amok Time*, Spock faces two of the greatest challenges in life when his wedding is interrupted by a fight to the death with his best friend, Captain Kirk. His betrothed, T'Pring has enforced this dual as part of a plan to secure her future by inheriting Spock's fortune.

In the episode *All Our Yesterdays*, Spock and McCoy step back in time 5000 years. In this Ice Age environment we are given further insights into Spock's personality. His relationship with McCoy is also put to the test. ∎

JANUARY						1996		FEBRUARY						1996		MARCH						1996
M	T	W	T	F	S	S		M	T	W	T	F	S	S		M	T	W	T	F	S	S

JANUARY 1996
M T W T F S S
1 2 3 4 5 6 7
8 9 10 11 12 13 14
15 16 17 18 19 20 21
22 23 24 25 26 27 28
29 30 31

FEBRUARY 1996
M T W T F S S
        1 2 3 4
5 6 7 8 9 10 11
12 13 14 15 16 17 18
19 20 21 22 23 24 25
26 27 28 29

MARCH 1996
M T W T F S S
        1 2 3
4 5 6 7 8 9 10
11 12 13 14 15 16 17
18 19 20 21 22 23 24
25 26 27 28 29 30 31

◀ FEBRUARY ▬

MONDAY 5

Waitangi Day (New Zealand)

TUESDAY 6

WEDNESDAY 7

Ethan Phillip's Birthday (Neelix)

THURSDAY 8

FRIDAY 9

SATURDAY 10

National Foundation Day (Japan)

SUNDAY 11

ALIEN CULTURES

The way of handling alien cultures is determined by the Prime Directive code of ethics. In *Elaan Of Troyius*, however, it is the ethics of the aliens that are under question, as Kirk battles to resist the mesmerising tears of Elaan.

The fierce yet honourable Klingons make their first ever appearance in the original STAR TREK® series episode *Errand Of Mercy*. Commander Kor, played flawlessly by John Colicos, sets the standard for the characterisation of the entire Klingon culture, an important dimension in the STAR TREK universe. ■

JANUARY						1996		FEBRUARY						1996		MARCH						1996
M	T	W	T	F	S	S		M	T	W	T	F	S	S		M	T	W	T	F	S	S
1	2	3	4	5	6	7					1	2	3	4						1	2	3
8	9	10	11	12	13	14		5	6	7	8	9	10	11		4	5	6	7	8	9	10
15	16	17	18	19	20	21		12	13	14	15	16	17	18		11	12	13	14	15	16	17
22	23	24	25	26	27	28		19	20	21	22	23	24	25		18	19	20	21	22	23	24
29	30	31						26	27	28	29					25	26	27	28	29	30	31

◀ FEBRUARY ▬▬

MONDAY 12

Susan Oliver's Birthday (Vina)

TUESDAY 13

WEDNESDAY 14

St Valentine's Day

THURSDAY 15

FRIDAY 16

SATURDAY 17

SUNDAY 18

COMMAND DECISION

10045

10046

10047

10048

In *The Enterprise Incident*, Spock's diplomatic skills and Kirk's acting skills are employed to trick the Romulan Commander out of her cloaking device.

Lieutenant Uhura is not intimidated by conman Harcourt Fenton Mudd, in the episode, *I, Mudd*, which sees him utilising hundreds of androids in pursuit of his greedy needs. Mudd gets his just desserts when he is stranded with 500 android replicas of his nerve-shattering wife Stella. ∎

	JANUARY				1996			FEBRUARY				1996			MARCH				1996	
M	T	W	T	F	S	S	M	T	W	T	F	S	S	M	T	W	T	F	S	S
1	2	3	4	5	6	7				1	2	3	4					1	2	3
8	9	10	11	12	13	14	5	6	7	8	9	10	11	4	5	6	7	8	9	10
15	16	17	18	19	20	21	12	13	14	15	16	17	18	11	12	13	14	15	16	17
22	23	24	25	26	27	28	19	20	21	22	23	24	25	18	19	20	21	22	23	24
29	30	31					26	27	28	29				25	26	27	28	29	30	31

◀ FEBRUARY ▬

New Year's Day (China)
President's Day (George Washington's Birthday) (USA)

MONDAY 19

TUESDAY 20

Ash Wednesday

WEDNESDAY 21

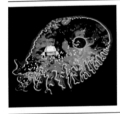

The Amoeba in Immunity Syndrome.

THURSDAY 22

Majel Barrett's Birthday (Nurse Chapel, Lwaxana Troi, ship's computer voice)

FRIDAY 23

SATURDAY 24

SUNDAY 25

In the perennial favourite *The Trouble With Tribbles*, penned by David Gerrold, Kirk has to deal with an array of problems from a rigid Federation official to the 'merchandise' of Cyrano Jones — the endlessly proliferating tribbles.

Genetically engineered superman Khan Noonian Singh (played by guest star Ricardo Montalban), meets his match in Captain Kirk. In this classic episode, *Space Seed*, the S.S. Botany Bay is discovered drifting in space. This episode was the catalyst for the popular motion picture STAR TREK® II: THE WRATH OF KHAN™. ∎

FEBRUARY					1996		MARCH					1996		APRIL					1996	
M	T	W	T	F	S	S	M	T	W	T	F	S	S	M	T	W	T	F	S	S
			1	2	3	4					1	2	3	1	2	3	4	5	6	7
5	6	7	8	9	10	11	4	5	6	7	8	9	10	8	9	10	11	12	13	14
12	13	14	15	16	17	18	11	12	13	14	15	16	17	15	16	17	18	19	20	21
19	20	21	22	23	24	25	18	19	20	21	22	23	24	22	23	24	25	26	27	28
26	27	28	29				25	26	27	28	29	30	31	29	30					

FEBRUARY - MARCH

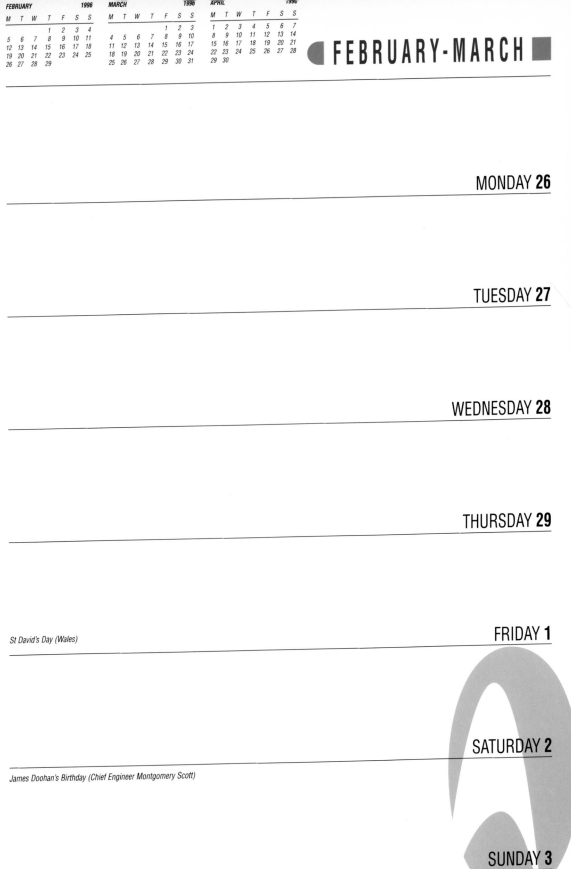

MONDAY 26

TUESDAY 27

WEDNESDAY 28

THURSDAY 29

St David's Day (Wales)

FRIDAY 1

SATURDAY 2

James Doohan's Birthday (Chief Engineer Montgomery Scott)

SUNDAY 3

10045

10046

10047

In *The City On The Edge Of Forever*, Captain Kirk utters the famous words: "Let's get the hell out of here." Sadly, Kirk has to allow the death of Edith Keeler (played by Joan Collins) so that the future may be kept intact. A classic episode many judge to be the best original series episode, beautifully penned by Harlan Ellison. ■

10048

FEBRUARY						1996		MARCH						1996		APRIL						1996
M	T	W	T	F	S	S		M	T	W	T	F	S	S		M	T	W	T	F	S	S
			1	2	3	4						1	2	3		1	2	3	4	5	6	7
5	6	7	8	9	10	11		4	5	6	7	8	9	10		8	9	10	11	12	13	14
12	13	14	15	16	17	18		11	12	13	14	15	16	17		15	16	17	18	19	20	21
19	20	21	22	23	24	25		18	19	20	21	22	23	24		22	23	24	25	26	27	28
26	27	28	29					25	26	27	28	29	30	31		29	30					

◀ MARCH ▬

MONDAY **4**

TUESDAY **5**

WEDNESDAY **6**

THURSDAY **7**

FRIDAY **8**

SATURDAY **9**

SUNDAY **10**

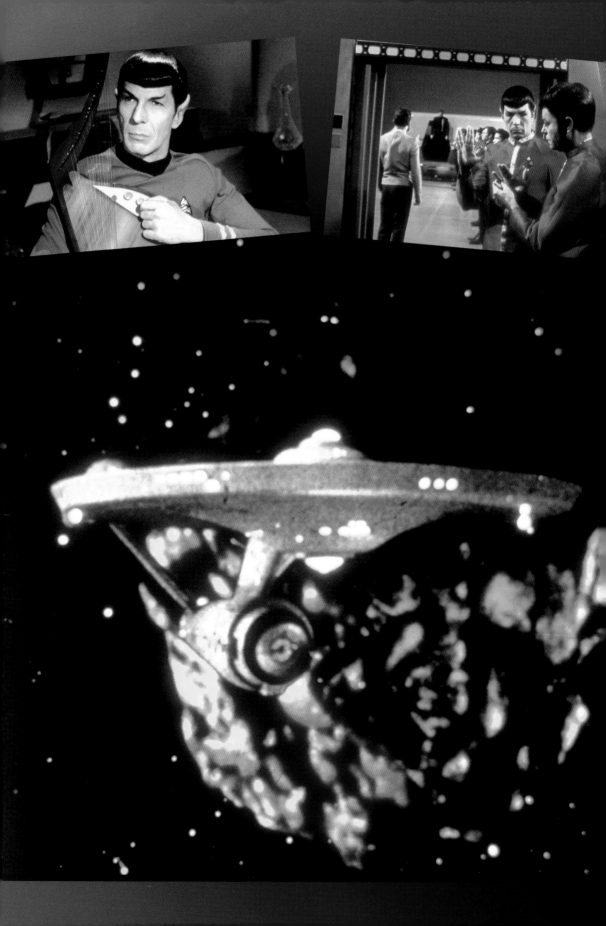

U.S.S. ENTERPRISE™ NCC-1701-D

616 784
891 884
241 681
337 987
854 254
994 **774**
824 321

The *U.S.S. Enterprise* is the flagship of Starfleet. This enormous galaxy class starship is equipped with the latest in technological advances, including a powerful computer system to assist during the exploration of space. Over 1000 people, crew and families, are housed aboard the ship, providing a microcosm away from Earth.

With such advanced features, the ship can go on extended missions, and carry out any orders Starfleet Command may deem necessary. Despite its huge size and large crew complement, the Starship Enterprise has a maximum warp speed in excess of factor 9.6. ■

784
884
681
987
254
774
321

FEBRUARY						1996		MARCH						1996		APRIL						1996
M	T	W	T	F	S	S		M	T	W	T	F	S	S		M	T	W	T	F	S	S
			1	2	3	4						1	2	3		1	2	3	4	5	6	7
5	6	7	8	9	10	11		4	5	6	7	8	9	10		8	9	10	11	12	13	14
12	13	14	15	16	17	18		11	12	13	14	15	16	17		15	16	17	18	19	20	21
19	20	21	22	23	24	25		18	19	20	21	22	23	24		22	23	24	25	26	27	28
26	27	28	29					25	26	27	28	29	30	31		29	30					

MONDAY 11

TUESDAY 12

Jonathan Frakes as Commander William T. Riker

WEDNESDAY 13

THURSDAY 14

FRIDAY 15

SATURDAY 16

St Patrick's Day (Republic of Ireland)
Bank Holiday (Northern Ireland)

SUNDAY 17

JEAN-LUC PICARD

10045

10046

10047

10048

In command of the awesome *U.S.S. Enterprise*™ is the experienced Captain Jean-Luc Picard. He is an officer with extraordinary skills in diplomacy and the ability to engender the highest respect from his crew. Although he holds the Prime Directive in high esteem, he is not afraid, when necessary, to beam down to a planet and use his powerful diplomatic abilities to maintain peace. ■

A busy starship captain needs to get away from the pressure of his position now and again, and Picard occasionally seeks solace with his family. Here he is pictured arriving at his brother's vineyard in France, accompanied by his beloved nephew, René, in *Family*.

This particular recreation period followed his horrific experience with the Borg, during which, as Locutus, he caused the death of several thousand Starfleet personnel. ■

| FEBRUARY | | | | | | 1996 |
M	T	W	T	F	S	S
			1	2	3	4
5	6	7	8	9	10	11
12	13	14	15	16	17	18
19	20	21	22	23	24	25
26	27	28	29			

| MARCH | | | | | | 1996 |
M	T	W	T	F	S	S
				1	2	3
4	5	6	7	8	9	10
11	12	13	14	15	16	17
18	19	20	21	22	23	24
25	26	27	28	29	30	31

| APRIL | | | | | | 1996 |
M	T	W	T	F	S	S
1	2	3	4	5	6	7
8	9	10	11	12	13	14
15	16	17	18	19	20	21
22	23	24	25	26	27	28
29	30					

MARCH

MONDAY **18**

TUESDAY **19**

Vernal Equinox Day (Japan, UK)

WEDNESDAY **20**

THURSDAY **21**

William Shatner's Birthday (Captain James T. Kirk)

FRIDAY **22**

SATURDAY **23**

SUNDAY **24**

In the episode *In Theory,* Data tries to sample the intimacy of a relationship with a fellow crewmate. Jenna is just recovering from a failed long-term relationship and finds Data's sensitivity appealing. The experience sadly proves to be disastrous, but it gives Data further valuable insight into what it means to be human. ■

One of the more interesting, although decidedly dangerous, scenarios for Data involves his aberrant sibling, Lore.
Whenever the evil Lore appears, trouble is certain to follow. Despite this, Data once again is able to add to his database, constantly absorbing more about humanity, even if it means dealing with Lore harshly.

Over the seven-year run of STAR TREK®: THE NEXT GENERATION™, Data has developed many different character nuances to the point where he is so close to being human, that he is often treated as such by his colleagues.

His sentience is no more succinctly demonstrated than in the episode *The Measure Of A Man*, in which Data is virtually forced to prove why he should not be dismantled and used for experimentation by a Starfleet scientist. With Picard at his side, Data mounts a superb defence, and easily wins the right to continue his existence. ■

FEBRUARY						1996		MARCH						1996		APRIL						1996
M	T	W	T	F	S	S		M	T	W	T	F	S	S		M	T	W	T	F	S	S
			1	2	3	4						1	2	3		1	2	3	4	5	6	7
5	6	7	8	9	10	11		4	5	6	7	8	9	10		8	9	10	11	12	13	14
12	13	14	15	16	17	18		11	12	13	14	15	16	17		15	16	17	18	19	20	21
19	20	21	22	23	24	25		18	19	20	21	22	23	24		22	23	24	25	26	27	28
26	27	28	29					25	26	27	28	29	30	31		29	30					

 **MARCH**

Annunciation

MONDAY 25

Leonard Nimoy's Birthday (Mr Spock)

TUESDAY 26

WEDNESDAY 27

THURSDAY 28

Marina Sirtis's Birthday (Counsellor Deanna Troi)

FRIDAY 29

SATURDAY 30

British Summer Time begins (UK)

SUNDAY 31

CAPTAIN JEAN-LUC PICARD, MEDIATOR

10045

10046

10047

10048

As well as being a fine captain, time and again Picard has shown himself to be an excellent mediator. In the episode *Future Imperfect*, his natural abilities are foreseen when a glimpse of what appears to be the future is presented to Commander Riker.

Under difficult circumstances in the episode *Sarek*, Picard plays host and diplomat during a visit by the great Vulcan ambassador Sarek, and his partner, Perrin. With aplomb and delicacy, he handles the ailing Sarek in a manner that allows the legendary ambassador's honour to remain intact. Not only is Sarek protected, but Picard personally takes the responsibility to preserve the Federation's delicate treaty negotiations. ■

MARCH					1996		APRIL					1996		MAY					1996	
M	T	W	T	F	S	S	M	T	W	T	F	S	S	M	T	W	T	F	S	S
				1	2	3	1	2	3	4	5	6	7			1	2	3	4	5
4	5	6	7	8	9	10	8	9	10	11	12	13	14	6	7	8	9	10	11	12
11	12	13	14	15	16	17	15	16	17	18	19	20	21	13	14	15	16	17	18	19
18	19	20	21	22	23	24	22	23	24	25	26	27	28	20	21	22	23	24	25	26
25	26	27	28	29	30	31	29	30						27	28	29	30	31		

◀ APRIL ◼

Grace Lee Whitney's Birthday (Yeoman Janice Rand)

April Fools' Day

MONDAY 1

TUESDAY 2

WEDNESDAY 3

U.S.S. Enterprise™ *NCC-1701-D*

THURSDAY 4

Bank Holiday (Scotland)
Good Friday

FRIDAY 5

SATURDAY 6

Easter Sunday

SUNDAY 7

THE TROUBLE WITH Q

One of the most colourful characters in STAR TREK®: THE NEXT GENERATION™ is undoubtedly Q. Played perfectly by John de Lancie, he is the personification of a mischievous boy in a man's body. Blessed with extraordinary powers, he ushers in the new crew in the first episode, *Encounter At Farpoint,* by putting them on trial at the start of their mission. After successfully defending his crew and all humanity, Picard somehow senses he has not seen the last of Q.

In the episode *Q-Pid,* Q whisks the senior bridge crew back to Sherwood Forest and proceeds to toy with them in the guise of the Sheriff Of Nottingham. ■

MARCH						1996
M	T	W	T	F	S	S
				1	2	3
4	5	6	7	8	9	10
11	12	13	14	15	16	17
18	19	20	21	22	23	24
25	26	27	28	29	30	31

APRIL						1996
M	T	W	T	F	S	S
1	2	3	4	5	6	7
8	9	10	11	12	13	14
15	16	17	18	19	20	21
22	23	24	25	26	27	28
29	30					

MAY						1996
M	T	W	T	F	S	S
		1	2	3	4	5
6	7	8	9	10	11	12
13	14	15	16	17	18	19
20	21	22	23	24	25	26
27	28	29	30	31		

 **APRIL**

Easter Monday

MONDAY 8

TUESDAY 9

WEDNESDAY 10

THURSDAY 11

FRIDAY 12

SATURDAY 13

SUNDAY 14

COUNSELLOR TROI

10045

10046

10047

10048

A ship with a huge crew complement such as the *U.S.S. Enterprise*™ will always need the services of a counsellor. This is particularly necessary on a very extended voyage. Counsellor Troi, a half human, half Betazoid female, has special empathic powers that enable her to provide support and help for all the crew.

A special relationship with Commander Riker already in place, Troi sets about becoming an invaluable confidante to Captain Picard and many others aboard the ship. ■

MARCH **1996**

M	T	W	T	F	S	S
				1	2	3
4	5	6	7	8	9	10
11	12	13	14	15	16	17
18	19	20	21	22	23	24
25	26	27	28	29	30	31

APRIL **1996**

M	T	W	T	F	S	S
1	2	3	4	5	6	7
8	9	10	11	12	13	14
15	16	17	18	19	20	21
22	23	24	25	26	27	28
29	30					

MAY **1996**

M	T	W	T	F	S	S
		1	2	3	4	5
6	7	8	9	10	11	12
13	14	15	16	17	18	19
20	21	22	23	24	25	26
27	28	29	30	31		

APRIL

MONDAY **15**

TUESDAY **16**

WEDNESDAY **17**

THURSDAY **18**

FRIDAY **19**

George Takei's Birthday (Captain Sulu)

SATURDAY **20**

SUNDAY **21**

SECURITY CHIEF WORF

10045

10046

10047

10048

Caught between two cultures and being the only Klingon in Starfleet has frequently made life very difficult for Lieutenant Worf. Still a fiercely proud and traditional Klingon, his Starfleet Academy days and his assignment on the *U.S.S. Enterprise™* have made him develop a quiet maturity.

Respected by his fellow officers and — finally — by the Klingon High Council, Lieutenant Worf has proved to be a master tactician, and a valuable security chief for Captain Picard. ■

MARCH						1996
M	T	W	T	F	S	S
				1	2	3
4	5	6	7	8	9	10
11	12	13	14	15	16	17
18	19	20	21	22	23	24
25	26	27	28	29	30	31

APRIL						1996
M	T	W	T	F	S	S
1	2	3	4	5	6	7
8	9	10	11	12	13	14
15	16	17	18	19	20	21
22	23	24	25	26	27	28
29	30					

MAY						1996
M	T	W	T	F	S	S
		1	2	3	4	5
6	7	8	9	10	11	12
13	14	15	16	17	18	19
20	21	22	23	24	25	26
27	28	29	30	31		

APRIL

Brent Spiner as Lieutenant Commander Data

MONDAY 22

TUESDAY 23

WEDNESDAY 24

Anzac Day (Australia, New Zealand)

THURSDAY 25

FRIDAY 26

SATURDAY 27

SUNDAY 28

The heart of the *U.S.S. Enterprise*™ is the engineering section. It is here that the mighty starship derives the great power that enables it to traverse space in the wink of an eye.

Chief Engineer, responsible for the smooth running of the huge engines, is Geordi La Forge. Being blind, he wears a special visor over his eyes, which provides his visual acuity. La Forge has proved to be very innovative, and he has used his engineering knowledge to rescue the crew and the ship on several occasions.

He has developed a special friendship with Data, but in the episode *Elementary, Dear Data*, this relationship is strained when Data's tremendous computing power undermines La Forge's fun during a holodeck sequence.

APRIL						1996
M	T	W	T	F	S	S
1	2	3	4	5	6	7
8	9	10	11	12	13	14
15	16	17	18	19	20	21
22	23	24	25	26	27	28
29	30					

MAY						1996
M	T	W	T	F	S	S
		1	2	3	4	5
6	7	8	9	10	11	12
13	14	15	16	17	18	19
20	21	22	23	24	25	26
27	28	29	30	31		

JUNE						1996
M	T	W	T	F	S	S
					1	2
3	4	5	6	7	8	9
10	11	12	13	14	15	16
17	18	19	20	21	22	23
24	25	26	27	28	29	30

Kate Mulgrew's Birthday (Captain Kathryn Janeway)

Greenery Day (Japan)

MONDAY 29

TUESDAY 30

Labour Day (May Day) (France)
May Day (Germany)

WEDNESDAY 1

THURSDAY 2

Constitution Day (Japan)

FRIDAY 3

SATURDAY 4

SUNDAY 5

The senior bridge crew of the *U.S.S. Enterprise* is comprised of the finest officers in Starfleet.

Together they epitomise the ideals and values that have made the Federation into a benevolent organisation able to peacefully extend its boundaries into known space and beyond. ■

Clockwise from centre:
Capt Picard (*Patrick Stewart*)
Counsellor Troi (*Marina Sirtis*)
Lt Cmdr La Forge (*LeVar Burton*)
Lt Cmdr Data (*Brent Spiner*)
Lt Worf (*Michael Dorn*)
Cmdr Riker (*Jonathan Frakes*)
Dr Crusher (*Gates McFadden*)

CREW OF U.S.S. ENTERPRISE™

APRIL						1996
M	T	W	T	F	S	S
1	2	3	4	5	6	7
8	9	10	11	12	13	14
15	16	17	18	19	20	21
22	23	24	25	26	27	28
29	30					

MAY						1996
M	T	W	T	F	S	S
		1	2	3	4	5
6	7	8	9	10	11	12
13	14	15	16	17	18	19
20	21	22	23	24	25	26
27	28	29	30	31		

JUNE						1996
M	T	W	T	F	S	S
					1	2
3	4	5	6	7	8	9
10	11	12	13	14	15	16
17	18	19	20	21	22	23
24	25	26	27	28	29	30

◀ MAY ▬

May Day Bank Holiday (UK and Republic of Ireland)

MONDAY **6**

TUESDAY **7**

VE Day (France)

WEDNESDAY **8**

THURSDAY **9**

FRIDAY **10**

SATURDAY **11**

SUNDAY **12**

Space Station Deep Space Nine is strategically important to Bajor and the Federation. It is helmed by Commander Sisko, with Major Kira as his first officer. Together with the other senior staff, they preside over this delicate gateway to the Wormhole, which leads to the Gamma Quadrant. ■

Clockwise from centre: Quark (*Armin Shimerman*), Lt Jadzia Dax (*Terry Farrell*), Constable Odo (*René Auberjonois*), Chief O'Brien (*Colm Meaney*), Jake Sisko (*Cirroc Lofton*), Commander Sisko (*Avery Brooks*), Major Kira (*Nana Visitor*), Dr Bashir (*Siddig El Fadil*).

THE HEART OF SPACE STATION DEEP SPACE NINE

APRIL						1996		MAY						1996		JUNE						1996
M	T	W	T	F	S	S		M	T	W	T	F	S	S		M	T	W	T	F	S	S
1	2	3	4	5	6	7				1	2	3	4	5							1	2
8	9	10	11	12	13	14		6	7	8	9	10	11	12		3	4	5	6	7	8	9
15	16	17	18	19	20	21		13	14	15	16	17	18	19		10	11	12	13	14	15	16
22	23	24	25	26	27	28		20	21	22	23	24	25	26		17	18	19	20	21	22	23
29	30							27	28	29	30	31				24	25	26	27	28	29	30

 **◀ MAY ▬**

MONDAY 13

TUESDAY 14

WEDNESDAY 15

Feast of the Ascension (France)

THURSDAY 16

FRIDAY 17

Terry Farrell as Lt Jadzia Dax

SATURDAY 18

SUNDAY 19

After a troubled start to life on board space station Deep Space Nine, Commander Sisko is now in full command, and has earned the respect of both the Bajoran government and the space station's former occupiers, the Cardassians. His strict command style, coupled with his excellent diplomatic tact, has enabled him to preserve the delicate balance of peace in this sector of the galaxy. ■

215847	4857	584669	21	3351
544871	5541	845751	299	24

An officer of great resolve and dedication, Sisko was forced to pick up the threads of his shattered life following the tragic death of his beloved wife, Jennifer. After the Borg attack at Wolf 359, Sisko was on the verge of retiring from Starfleet and from life.

A new command at Deep Space Nine, and the needs of his adolescent son Jake, enabled him to overcome the loss of his wife and to move forward.

In the pilot episode, *Emissary*, he brilliantly handled the delicate Federation take over of the space station after the Cardassian occupiers had retreated, leaving a stripped and almost ruined facility in their wake. From the moment that Kai Opaka, the spiritual leader of Bajor, sensed his soul, she knew he would be the man who could return respect and dignity to her war-ravaged people. ■

APRIL						1996		MAY						1996		JUNE						1996
M	T	W	T	F	S	S		M	T	W	T	F	S	S		M	T	W	T	F	S	S
1	2	3	4	5	6	7				1	2	3	4	5							1	2
8	9	10	11	12	13	14		6	7	8	9	10	11	12		3	4	5	6	7	8	9
15	16	17	18	19	20	21		13	14	15	16	17	18	19		10	11	12	13	14	15	16
22	23	24	25	26	27	28		20	21	22	23	24	25	26		17	18	19	20	21	22	23
29	30							27	28	29	30	31				24	25	26	27	28	29	30

 **MAY**

MONDAY **20**

TUESDAY **21**

WEDNESDAY **22**

THURSDAY **23**

FRIDAY **24**

SATURDAY **25**

Whitsunday (Germany)

SUNDAY **26**

MAJOR KIRA NERYS

10045

10046

10047

10048

Major Kira Nerys is the space station's first officer. A fiercely proud Bajoran, she has served her people as an underground resistance fighter, and is now an officer aboard the station.

Passionate and powerful, she finds that her work now is even more difficult, having to juggle the requirements of her commanding officer and the Federation with those of the Bajoran provisional government. ■

MAY							1996
M	T	W	T	F	S	S	
		1	2	3	4	5	
6	7	8	9	10	11	12	
13	14	15	16	17	18	19	
20	21	22	23	24	25	26	
27	28	29	30	31			

JUNE							1996
M	T	W	T	F	S	S	
					1	2	
3	4	5	6	7	8	9	
10	11	12	13	14	15	16	
17	18	19	20	21	22	23	
24	25	26	27	28	29	30	

JULY							1996
M	T	W	T	F	S	S	
1	2	3	4	5	6	7	
8	9	10	11	12	13	14	
15	16	17	18	19	20	21	
22	23	24	25	26	27	28	
29	30	31					

MAY-JUNE

Whitmonday (Germany)
Pentecost Day (France)
Spring Holiday (UK)
Bank Holiday (Scotland)
Memorial Day (USA)

MONDAY **27**

TUESDAY **28**

WEDNESDAY **29**

Michael Piller's Birthday (Executive Producer, ST: TNG, ST: DS9, ST: VOY; Co-Creator, ST: DS9, ST: VOY)

THURSDAY **30**

FRIDAY **31**

SATURDAY **1**

SUNDAY **2**

THE WORMHOLE, GATEWAY TO THE GAMMA QUADRANT

The first known stable wormhole in the galaxy was discovered by Commander Sisko and Lieutenant Dax during the initial Federation transfer of authority. Alien lifeforms are known to inhabit the wormhole, but they show no hostility to the multitude of travellers that pass through.

Its entrance is patrolled by Deep Space Nine and thus falls under the jurisdiction of Bajor. With the Cardassian threat not entirely removed, the strategic importance of this portal makes it a valuable economic factor in Bajor's rehabilitation, and a political hot-spot for the Federation.■

MAY						1996		JUNE						1996		JULY						1996
M	T	W	T	F	S	S		M	T	W	T	F	S	S		M	T	W	T	F	S	S
		1	2	3	4	5							1	2		1	2	3	4	5	6	7
6	7	8	9	10	11	12		3	4	5	6	7	8	9		8	9	10	11	12	13	14
13	14	15	16	17	18	19		10	11	12	13	14	15	16		15	16	17	18	19	20	21
20	21	22	23	24	25	26		17	18	19	20	21	22	23		22	23	24	25	26	27	28
27	28	29	30	31				24	25	26	27	28	29	30		29	30	31				

JUNE

Holiday (Republic of Ireland)
Queen's Birthday (Germany)

MONDAY 3

TUESDAY 4

WEDNESDAY 5

Jeri Taylor's Birthday (Executive Producer, ST: TNG, ST: VOY; Co-Creator ST: VOY)

THURSDAY 6

A dangerous Cardassian officer

FRIDAY 7

SATURDAY 8

SUNDAY 9

QUARK

616 784
891 884
241 681
337 987
854 254
994 **774**
824 321

Senior merchant on Deep Space Nine is Quark, an extremely shrewd Ferengi trader whose establishment does roaring trade in the promenade.

His legendary connections have enabled him to be very helpful (reluctantly — for there is no profit) to Commander Sisko on several occasions.

He is kept very tightly in check by the security chief of the space station, Constable Odo. ■

784
884
681
987
254
774
321

77453284
66224482

MAY					1996			JUNE					1996			JULY					1996	
M	T	W	T	F	S	S		M	T	W	T	F	S	S		M	T	W	T	F	S	S
		1	2	3	4	5							1	2		1	2	3	4	5	6	7
6	7	8	9	10	11	12		3	4	5	6	7	8	9		8	9	10	11	12	13	14
13	14	15	16	17	18	19		10	11	12	13	14	15	16		15	16	17	18	19	20	21
20	21	22	23	24	25	26		17	18	19	20	21	22	23		22	23	24	25	26	27	28
27	28	29	30	31				24	25	26	27	28	29	30		29	30	31				

JUNE

Queen's Birthday Holiday (Australia)

MONDAY **10**

TUESDAY **11**

WEDNESDAY **12**

THURSDAY **13**

FRIDAY **14**

SATURDAY **15**

SUNDAY **16**

DR JULIAN BASHIR

The resident medical officer and *ST:DS:9*'s 'Mr Adventure' is the young and brilliant Dr Julian Bashir.

In the episode shown here, *Distant Voices*, he seems to have contracted a disease that has made him age rapidly, but this has not diminished his appeal to the opposite sex. ∎

```
215847    4857    584669  21   3351
544871    5541    845751  299  24
```

After graduating second from medical school (a minor slip robbed him of first place), Bashir opted for an adventurous transfer, ending up on Deep Space Nine. Despite an early confrontation with Major Kira after he naively referred to Bajor as a remote wilderness, he has settled down to become a key member of the space station. He has excelled himself by coming up with some empirical solutions in tight situations.

His one small failing is a quite uncontrollable crush on Jadzia Dax but this has not prevented him from providing high quality medical care in this alien and somewhat inhospitable part of the galaxy. ∎

MAY						1996		JUNE						1996		JULY						1996
M	T	W	T	F	S	S		M	T	W	T	F	S	S		M	T	W	T	F	S	S
		1	2	3	4	5							1	2		1	2	3	4	5	6	7
6	7	8	9	10	11	12		3	4	5	6	7	8	9		8	9	10	11	12	13	14
13	14	15	16	17	18	19		10	11	12	13	14	15	16		15	16	17	18	19	20	21
20	21	22	23	24	25	26		17	18	19	20	21	22	23		22	23	24	25	26	27	28
27	28	29	30	31				24	25	26	27	28	29	30		29	30	31				

JUNE

MONDAY 17

TUESDAY 18

WEDNESDAY 19

THURSDAY 20

FRIDAY 21

Tim Russ' Birthday (Tactical and Security Officer Mr Tuvok)

SATURDAY 22

SUNDAY 23

Chief of Security Odo has a difficult job on the space station. Not only does he have to keep the peace between myriad alien travellers and the inhabitants of the station, he also struggles to be at peace with himself. A mysterious shapeshifter, he was discovered and brought up by a Bajoran scientist on Bajor.

Miraculously, his constant quest to define himself and to discover his origins has not stopped him from maintaining law and order on the space station. Two of his persistent problems in routine security work are the antics of Quark and the Cardassian clothing store proprietor Garak, seen here having a difference of opinion. ■

MAY						1996
M	T	W	T	F	S	S
		1	2	3	4	5
6	7	8	9	10	11	12
13	14	15	16	17	18	19
20	21	22	23	24	25	26
27	28	29	30	31		

JUNE						1996
M	T	W	T	F	S	S
					1	2
3	4	5	6	7	8	9
10	11	12	13	14	15	16
17	18	19	20	21	22	23
24	25	26	27	28	29	30

JULY						1996
M	T	W	T	F	S	S
1	2	3	4	5	6	7
8	9	10	11	12	13	14
15	16	17	18	19	20	21
22	23	24	25	26	27	28
29	30	31				

JUNE

MONDAY 24

Siddig El Fadil as Dr Julian Bashir

TUESDAY 25

WEDNESDAY 26

THURSDAY 27

FRIDAY 28

SATURDAY 29

SUNDAY 30

CHIEF ENGINEER O'BRIEN

10045

10046

10047

Chief engineer and miracle worker for the space station is Miles O'Brien, who transferred from the *U.S.S. Enterprise*™ to take a promotion. A technical wizard, his only real problem is striving to maintain a fruitful and satisfying way of life for his wife Keiko, a trained botanist, and daughter Molly. ■

10048

JUNE						1996	JULY						1996	AUGUST						1996
M	T	W	T	F	S	S	M	T	W	T	F	S	S	M	T	W	T	F	S	S
					1	2	1	2	3	4	5	6	7				1	2	3	4
3	4	5	6	7	8	9	8	9	10	11	12	13	14	5	6	7	8	9	10	11
10	11	12	13	14	15	16	15	16	17	18	19	20	21	12	13	14	15	16	17	18
17	18	19	20	21	22	23	22	23	24	25	26	27	28	19	20	21	22	23	24	25
24	25	26	27	28	29	30	29	30	31					26	27	28	29	30	31	

 **JULY**

MONDAY 1

TUESDAY 2

WEDNESDAY 3

Independence Day (USA) **THURSDAY 4**

FRIDAY 5

SATURDAY 6

SUNDAY 7

SCIENCE OFFICER JADZIA DAX

616 784
891 884
241 681
337 987
854 254
994 774
824 321

Science Officer Lieutenant Jadzia Dax is a Trill. Her symbiont is Dax, who used to be a close friend of Sisko, when the host body was Curzon.

She has settled into a close working relationship and friendship with Sisko, who has had to get used to her 28-year-old female host body. This has not been easy for Sisko, having been Curzon's protégé for so many years - the switch from an old man to a young female has been very disconcerting!

Every bit as passionate as Kira, but in a different way, she has proven her mettle time and again, and seems to be taking pleasure in fending off the amorous Bashir with aplomb. ■

784
884
681
987
254
774
321

77453284
66224482

JUNE						1996
M	T	W	T	F	S	S
					1	2
3	4	5	6	7	8	9
10	11	12	13	14	15	16
17	18	19	20	21	22	23
24	25	26	27	28	29	30

JULY						1996
M	T	W	T	F	S	S
1	2	3	4	5	6	7
8	9	10	11	12	13	14
15	16	17	18	19	20	21
22	23	24	25	26	27	28
29	30	31				

AUGUST						1996
M	T	W	T	F	S	S
			1	2	3	4
5	6	7	8	9	10	11
12	13	14	15	16	17	18
19	20	21	22	23	24	25
26	27	28	29	30	31	

◀ JULY ▬▬

MONDAY **8**

TUESDAY **9**

WEDNESDAY **10**

THURSDAY **11**

FRIDAY **12**

Patrick Stewart's Birthday (Captain Jean-Luc Picard)

SATURDAY **13**

Bastille Day (France)

SUNDAY **14**

In season three, Commander Sisko has the pleasure of taking command of the powerful *Defiant*, the resident flagship of Deep Space Nine. This very powerful Federation ship is a unique vessel that was developed to fend off the dreaded Borg, the race of part human, part machines, but it has since been retired from that duty.

It is the only Federation vessel equipped with a fully functional cloaking device and has added much needed strength to the arsenal of Deep Space Nine. ∎

77453284
66224482

616 784
891 884
241 681
337 987
854 254
994 **774**
824 321

JUNE						1996
M	T	W	T	F	S	S
					1	2
3	4	5	6	7	8	9
10	11	12	13	14	15	16
17	18	19	20	21	22	23
24	25	26	27	28	29	30

JULY						1996
M	T	W	T	F	S	S
1	2	3	4	5	6	7
8	9	10	11	12	13	14
15	16	17	18	19	20	21
22	23	24	25	26	27	28
29	30	31				

AUGUST						1996
M	T	W	T	F	S	S
			1	2	3	4
5	6	7	8	9	10	11
12	13	14	15	16	17	18
19	20	21	22	23	24	25
26	27	28	29	30	31	

JULY

MONDAY 15

TUESDAY 16

WEDNESDAY 17

Armin Shimerman as the Ferengi Quark

THURSDAY 18

FRIDAY 19

SATURDAY 20

SUNDAY 21

JAKE SISKO

10045

10046

10047

Jake Sisko has not had an easy childhood. As the son of a Starfleet officer, he has always experienced upheaval as his parents moved from post to post. Far from interfering with his development, however, it has provided a wealth of experience, and enabled him to cope with the premature death of his mother.

Apart from the physical death of his mother, the toughest problem he has had to face so far is the 'spiritual death' of his father. The re-location to Deep Space Nine and the rejuvenation of his father's spirits, however, have once again put him on the track to maturity. ■

10048

JUNE						1996
M	T	W	T	F	S	S
					1	2
3	4	5	6	7	8	9
10	11	12	13	14	15	16
17	18	19	20	21	22	23
24	25	26	27	28	29	30

JULY						1996
M	T	W	T	F	S	S
1	2	3	4	5	6	7
8	9	10	11	12	13	14
15	16	17	18	19	20	21
22	23	24	25	26	27	28
29	30	31				

AUGUST						1996
M	T	W	T	F	S	S
			1	2	3	4
5	6	7	8	9	10	11
12	13	14	15	16	17	18
19	20	21	22	23	24	25
26	27	28	29	30	31	

JULY

MONDAY **22**

TUESDAY **23**

WEDNESDAY **24**

THURSDAY **25**

FRIDAY **26**

SATURDAY **27**

SUNDAY **28**

From left of page:
Ensign Harry Kim (*Garrett Wang*)
Lt Tom Paris (*Robert Duncan McNeil*)
Neelix (*Ethan West*)
Kes (*Jennifer Lien*)
Captain Janeway (*Kate Mulgrew*)
B'Elanna Torres (*Roxann Biggs-Dawson*)
Mr Tuvok (*Tim Russ*)
The Doctor (*Robert Picardo*)
Chakotay (*Robert Beltran*)

The hybrid crew, brought together by necessity and circumstance, comprises Federation officers, Maquis rebels, a holographic doctor, and two aliens from the Delta Quadrant.

Under the command of Captain Kathryn Janeway, their mission is to find a way back to the known Federation sector in space, some 75 light years away! ■

CREW OF THE U.S.S. VOYAGER™

JULY						1996
M	T	W	T	F	S	S
1	2	3	4	5	6	7
8	9	10	11	12	13	14
15	16	17	18	19	20	21
22	23	24	25	26	27	28
29	30	31				

AUGUST						1996
M	T	W	T	F	S	S
			1	2	3	4
5	6	7	8	9	10	11
12	13	14	15	16	17	18
19	20	21	22	23	24	25
26	27	28	29	30	31	

SEPTEMBER						1996
M	T	W	T	F	S	S
30						1
2	3	4	5	6	7	8
9	10	11	12	13	14	15
16	17	18	19	20	21	22
23	24	25	26	27	28	29

JULY-AUGUST

Wil Wheaton's Birthday (Ensign Wesley Crusher)

MONDAY **29**

TUESDAY **30**

WEDNESDAY **31**

THURSDAY **1**

FRIDAY **2**

SATURDAY **3**

SUNDAY **4**

Chakotay, a native American and rebel Maquis captain, agrees to serve under Captain Janeway of the *U.S.S. Voyager*™ as first officer. His other function is to see that the remnants of his crew adjust to working within the confines of Starfleet in order to get back to known space. ■

| 215847 | 4857 | 584669 | 21 | 3351 |
| 544871 | 5541 | 845751 | 299 | 24 |

As well as being a brilliant starship captain, Kathryn Janeway is also a scientist. This provides her with a broader base of information from which to derive solutions.

She has to lead not only the remainder of her commissioned crew, but must also earn the respect and loyalty of the Maquis who now serve aboard.

Through sheer strength and presence, she proves to be a charismatic leader in the same style as the legendary Captain Kirk. ■

JULY						1996
M	T	W	T	F	S	S
1	2	3	4	5	6	7
8	9	10	11	12	13	14
15	16	17	18	19	20	21
22	23	24	25	26	27	28
29	30	31				

AUGUST						1996
M	T	W	T	F	S	S
			1	2	3	4
5	6	7	8	9	10	11
12	13	14	15	16	17	18
19	20	21	22	23	24	25
26	27	28	29	30	31	

SEPTEMBER						1996
M	T	W	T	F	S	S
30						1
2	3	4	5	6	7	8
9	10	11	12	13	14	15
16	17	18	19	20	21	22
23	24	25	26	27	28	29

◀ AUGUST ▬▬

Holiday (Republic of Ireland)
Bank Holiday (Scotland)

MONDAY 5

TUESDAY 6

Kate Mulgrew as Captain Kathryn Janeway

WEDNESDAY 7

THURSDAY 8

FRIDAY 9

SATURDAY 10

SUNDAY 11

CARETAKER

10045

10046

10047

10048

In the pilot episode *Caretaker,* Captain Janeway encounters the alien entity that can return her ship and crew to the known universe.

Weighted by the knowledge that he is no longer able to look after the planet, the entity (in the shape of an old banjo-playing man), refuses to help her. ■

JULY						1996
M	T	W	T	F	S	S
1	2	3	4	5	6	7
8	9	10	11	12	13	14
15	16	17	18	19	20	21
22	23	24	25	26	27	28
29	30	31				

AUGUST						1996
M	T	W	T	F	S	S
			1	2	3	4
5	6	7	8	9	10	11
12	13	14	15	16	17	18
19	20	21	22	23	24	25
26	27	28	29	30	31	

SEPTEMBER						1996
M	T	W	T	F	S	S
30						1
2	3	4	5	6	7	8
9	10	11	12	13	14	15
16	17	18	19	20	21	22
23	24	25	26	27	28	29

◀ **AUGUST** ▬▬▬

MONDAY **12**

TUESDAY **13**

WEDNESDAY **14**

THURSDAY **15**

FRIDAY **16**

SATURDAY **17**

SUNDAY **18**

Chief Engineer aboard the *U.S.S. Voyager*™ is the former Maquis rebel B'Elanna Torres. As if being a Maquis is not enough, this passionate and complex young woman also has the fire of Klingon blood in her veins — something with which she is still trying to come to terms.

Although she dropped out of Starfleet Academy to join the Maquis, she is a brilliant engineer. Her flair is recognised by Chakotay and Janeway. In the episode *Parallax,* during a tussle for the top job, she displays the skills under fire that are to make Janeway's decision easy. As the latest member of the "miracle worker club", B'Elanna Torres has a lot to live up to. ∎

JULY						1996
M	T	W	T	F	S	S
1	2	3	4	5	6	7
8	9	10	11	12	13	14
15	16	17	18	19	20	21
22	23	24	25	26	27	28
29	30	31				

AUGUST						1996
M	T	W	T	F	S	S
			1	2	3	4
5	6	7	8	9	10	11
12	13	14	15	16	17	18
19	20	21	22	23	24	25
26	27	28	29	30	31	

SEPTEMBER						1996
M	T	W	T	F	S	S
30						1
2	3	4	5	6	7	8
9	10	11	12	13	14	15
16	17	18	19	20	21	22
23	24	25	26	27	28	29

◖ AUGUST ▬

Gene Roddenberry's Birthday (STAR TREK® Creator and Executive Producer)
Jonathan Frakes' Birthday (Commander William T. Riker)

MONDAY **19**

TUESDAY **20**

WEDNESDAY **21**

THURSDAY **22**

FRIDAY **23**

Jennifer Lien's Birthday (Kes)

SATURDAY **24**

SUNDAY **25**

THE FALL AND RISE OF TOM PARIS

After being expelled from Starfleet Academy, Tom Paris languished in a penal colony in New Zealand. His rehabilitation occurs in *Caretaker*, when Captain Janeway calls for his assistance. His mission? To inform on some former Maquis colleagues.

Despite this inauspicious beginning, Paris acquits himself well enough to be promoted quickly from observer to lieutenant. ∎

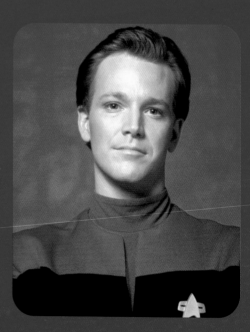

AUGUST						1996		SEPTEMBER						1996		OCTOBER						1996
M	T	W	T	F	S	S		M	T	W	T	F	S	S		M	T	W	T	F	S	S
			1	2	3	4		30						1			1	2	3	4	5	6
5	6	7	8	9	10	11		2	3	4	5	6	7	8		7	8	9	10	11	12	13
12	13	14	15	16	17	18		9	10	11	12	13	14	15		14	15	16	17	18	19	20
19	20	21	22	23	24	25		16	17	18	19	20	21	22		21	22	23	24	25	26	27
26	27	28	29	30	31			23	24	25	26	27	28	29		28	29	30	31			

AUGUST-SEPTEMBER

Late Summer Holiday (UK, not Scotland)

MONDAY **26**

TUESDAY **27**

Gates McFadden's Birthday (Dr Beverly Crusher)

WEDNESDAY **28**

THURSDAY **29**

Robert Duncan McNeill as Lt. Tom Paris

FRIDAY **30**

SATURDAY **31**

SUNDAY **1**

616 784
891 884
241 681
337 987
854 254
994 **774**
824 321

Alien junk trader Neelix and his companion Kes help the *U.S.S. Voyager*™ crew in the pilot episode, *Caretaker*.

Seeking a better way of life, they appeal to Captain Janeway for asylum on the ship in exchange for their help whenever alien species and strange planets are encountered. Kes is a member of the Ocampa race of beings who are interesting because their life span is only nine years. At the tender age of one she must show skills aboard the *U.S.S. Voyager*™ to earn her place among the crew. ∎

784
884
681
987
254
774
321

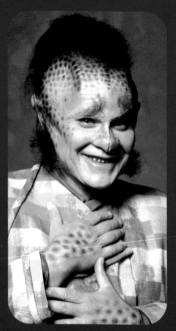

AUGUST						1996
M	T	W	T	F	S	S
			1	2	3	4
5	6	7	8	9	10	11
12	13	14	15	16	17	18
19	20	21	22	23	24	25
26	27	28	29	30	31	

SEPTEMBER						1996
M	T	W	T	F	S	S
30						1
2	3	4	5	6	7	8
9	10	11	12	13	14	15
16	17	18	19	20	21	22
23	24	25	26	27	28	29

OCTOBER						1996
M	T	W	T	F	S	S
	1	2	3	4	5	6
7	8	9	10	11	12	13
14	15	16	17	18	19	20
21	22	23	24	25	26	27
28	29	30	31			

SEPTEMBER

Labour Day (USA)

MONDAY **2**

TUESDAY **3**

WEDNESDAY **4**

THURSDAY **5**

FRIDAY **6**

SATURDAY **7**

SUNDAY **8**

U.S.S. VOYAGER™

616 784
891 884
241 681
337 987
854 254
994 **774**
824 321

Although the intrepid class *U.S.S. Voyager* is a smaller vessel than the galaxy class *U.S.S. Enterprise*™ NCC-1701-D, it is as technologically advanced as the larger craft.

Its special capabilities include a very long distance voyaging range with the speed and scientific power that allow it and its crew of 150 to explore the farthest reaches of the universe. ■

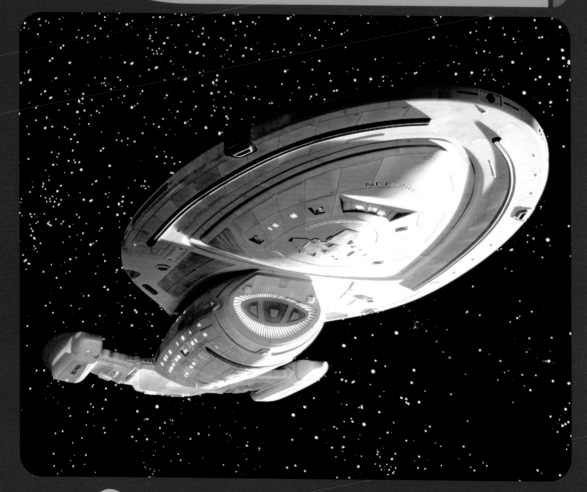

AUGUST						1996
M	T	W	T	F	S	S
			1	2	3	4
5	6	7	8	9	10	11
12	13	14	15	16	17	18
19	20	21	22	23	24	25
26	27	28	29	30	31	

SEPTEMBER						1996
M	T	W	T	F	S	S
30						1
2	3	4	5	6	7	8
9	10	11	12	13	14	15
16	17	18	19	20	21	22
23	24	25	26	27	28	29

OCTOBER						1996
M	T	W	T	F	S	S
	1	2	3	4	5	6
7	8	9	10	11	12	13
14	15	16	17	18	19	20
21	22	23	24	25	26	27
28	29	30	31			

SEPTEMBER

MONDAY 9

TUESDAY 10

Roxann Biggs-Dawson's Birthday (Chief Engineer B'Elanna Torres)

WEDNESDAY 11

THURSDAY 12

FRIDAY 13

Walter Koenig's Birthday (Commander Pavel Chekov)

SATURDAY 14

Respect for the Age Day (Japan)

SUNDAY 15

10045

10046

10047

The awe-inspiring bridge of the *U.S.S. Voyager*™ was designed by Richard James. With its brushed aluminium trimmings and all the latest accoutrements, it is easy to monitor everything happening aboard and beyond the ship.

The sick bay is the domain of the holographic program Doc Zimmerman. Encompassing the education and experiences of 46 medical officers, he is the epitome of the perfect doctor — except for his acute lack of bedside manner. ■

10048

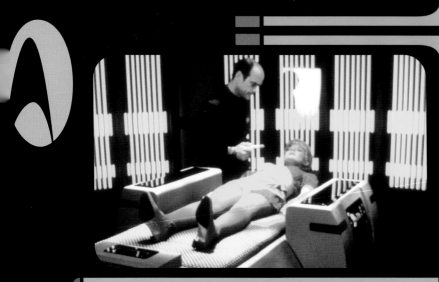

AUGUST						1996
M	T	W	T	F	S	S
			1	2	3	4
5	6	7	8	9	10	11
12	13	14	15	16	17	18
19	20	21	22	23	24	25
26	27	28	29	30	31	

SEPTEMBER						1996
M	T	W	T	F	S	S
30						1
2	3	4	5	6	7	8
9	10	11	12	13	14	15
16	17	18	19	20	21	22
23	24	25	26	27	28	29

OCTOBER						1996
M	T	W	T	F	S	S
	1	2	3	4	5	6
7	8	9	10	11	12	13
14	15	16	17	18	19	20
21	22	23	24	25	26	27
28	29	30	31			

◀ SEPTEMBER ▶

MONDAY **16**

TUESDAY **17**

Tim Russ as Security Officer Mr Tuvok

WEDNESDAY **18**

THURSDAY **19**

FRIDAY **20**

SATURDAY **21**

Autumnal Equinox Day (Japan, UK)

SUNDAY **22**

SECURITY OFFICER

Security officer aboard the *U.S.S. Voyager*™ is the Vulcan Mr Tuvok. While working undercover for the Federation, he infiltrated Chakotay's rebel Maquis ship. This is why he holds his current assignment.

A fiercely loyal and logical officer, he shares a close friendship with his commanding officer, Captain Janeway. ■

616 784
891 884
241 681
337 987
854 254
994 774
824 321

AUGUST						1996
M	T	W	T	F	S	S
			1	2	3	4
5	6	7	8	9	10	11
12	13	14	15	16	17	18
19	20	21	22	23	24	25
26	27	28	29	30	31	

SEPTEMBER						1996
M	T	W	T	F	S	S
30						1
2	3	4	5	6	7	8
9	10	11	12	13	14	15
16	17	18	19	20	21	22
23	24	25	26	27	28	29

OCTOBER						1996
M	T	W	T	F	S	S
	1	2	3	4	5	6
7	8	9	10	11	12	13
14	15	16	17	18	19	20
21	22	23	24	25	26	27
28	29	30	31			

SEPTEMBER

MONDAY **23**

TUESDAY **24**

WEDNESDAY **25**

THURSDAY **26**

FRIDAY **27**

SATURDAY **28**

SUNDAY **29**

SEPTEMBER						1996
M	T	W	T	F	S	S
30						1
2	3	4	5	6	7	8
9	10	11	12	13	14	15
16	17	18	19	20	21	22
23	24	25	26	27	28	29

OCTOBER						1996
M	T	W	T	F	S	S
	1	2	3	4	5	6
7	8	9	10	11	12	13
14	15	16	17	18	19	20
21	22	23	24	25	26	27
28	29	30	31			

NOVEMBER						1996
M	T	W	T	F	S	S
				1	2	3
4	5	6	7	8	9	10
11	12	13	14	15	16	17
18	19	20	21	22	23	24
25	26	27	28	29	30	

◖ SEPTEMBER-OCTOBER ∎

MONDAY 30

Mark Lenard's Birthday (Ambassador Sarek)

TUESDAY 1

WEDNESDAY 2

Day of German Unity (National Day) (Germany)

THURSDAY 3

FRIDAY 4

SATURDAY 5

SUNDAY 6

STAR TREK®: THE MOTION PICTURE™

616 784
891 884
241 681
337 987
854 254
994 **774**
824 321

In the first feature film, Kirk re-assumes command of the *U.S.S. Enterprise*™, taking over from Captain Willard Decker. His mission is to intercept the alien vessel that is rapidly closing in on Earth.

In the ensuing adventure, the alien vessel turns out to be the old Earth probe Voyager, which has been missing in space for a long time. ■

784
884
681
987
254
774
321

SEPTEMBER						1996
M	T	W	T	F	S	S
30						1
2	3	4	5	6	7	8
9	10	11	12	13	14	15
16	17	18	19	20	21	22
23	24	25	26	27	28	29

OCTOBER						1996
M	T	W	T	F	S	S
	1	2	3	4	5	6
7	8	9	10	11	12	13
14	15	16	17	18	19	20
21	22	23	24	25	26	27
28	29	30	31			

NOVEMBER						1996
M	T	W	T	F	S	S
				1	2	3
4	5	6	7	8	9	10
11	12	13	14	15	16	17
18	19	20	21	22	23	24
25	26	27	28	29	30	

◖ OCTOBER ▬

William Shatner as Captain James T. Kirk

MONDAY 7

TUESDAY 8

WEDNESDAY 9

Health Sports Day (Japan)

THURSDAY 10

FRIDAY 11

Spanish National Day (Spain)

SATURDAY 12

SUNDAY 13

STAR TREK® II: THE WRATH OF KHAN™

616 784
891 884
241 681
337 987
854 254
994 **774**
824 321

Captain Kirk faces his old foe Khan, who has survived Alpha Ceti V's orbital shift, and is ready to exact revenge for his 15-year banishment.

As well as being re-acquainted with Dr Carol Marcus, Kirk meets for the first time their son David, a proud and passionate young scientist. Kirk suffers a terrible loss when Spock, for the good of many, sacrifices his life, and saves the *U.S.S. Enterprise™*. ■

784
884
681
987
254
774   77453284
321   66224482

SEPTEMBER						1996		OCTOBER						1996		NOVEMBER						1996
M	T	W	T	F	S	S		M	T	W	T	F	S	S		M	T	W	T	F	S	S
30						1			1	2	3	4	5	6						1	2	3
2	3	4	5	6	7	8		7	8	9	10	11	12	13		4	5	6	7	8	9	10
9	10	11	12	13	14	15		14	15	16	17	18	19	20		11	12	13	14	15	16	17
16	17	18	19	20	21	22		21	22	23	24	25	26	27		18	19	20	21	22	23	24
23	24	25	26	27	28	29		28	29	30	31					25	26	27	28	29	30	

 OCTOBER

Columbus Day (USA)

MONDAY **14**

TUESDAY **15**

WEDNESDAY **16**

THURSDAY **17**

FRIDAY **18**

SATURDAY **19**

SUNDAY **20**

STAR TREK® III: THE SEARCH FOR SPOCK

616	784
891	884
241	681
337	987
854	254
994	**774**
824	321

Kirk encounters the wrath, not only of Starfleet, but also of the Klingo
when he misappropriates the soon-to-be decommissioned *U.S.S. Enterpris*
to seek out the Genesis planet and to solve the mystery of Spock's death
    Kruge, played by Christopher Lloyd, is Kirk's Klingon adversary, and
responsible for giving the order that causes the death of Kirk's son, Da
Marcus. Dr McCoy's mind, meanwhile, becomes the receptacle for Spoc
katra. He goes through hell until he is able to endure the refusion of Spo
in a ceremony which takes place on Vulcan. ■

784	
884	
681	
987	
254	
774	77453284
321	66224482

SEPTEMBER						1996	OCTOBER						1996	NOVEMBER						1996
M	T	W	T	F	S	S	M	T	W	T	F	S	S	M	T	W	T	F	S	S
30						1		1	2	3	4	5	6					1	2	3
2	3	4	5	6	7	8	7	8	9	10	11	12	13	4	5	6	7	8	9	10
9	10	11	12	13	14	15	14	15	16	17	18	19	20	11	12	13	14	15	16	17
16	17	18	19	20	21	22	21	22	23	24	25	26	27	18	19	20	21	22	23	24
23	24	25	26	27	28	29	28	29	30	31				25	26	27	28	29	30	

 **OCTOBER**

MONDAY **21**

TUESDAY **22**

WEDNESDAY **23**

THURSDAY **24**

FRIDAY **25**

SATURDAY **26**

Robert Picardo's Birthday (Emergency Holographic Medical Program)

British Summer Time ends (UK)

SUNDAY **27**

STAR TREK® IV: THE VOYAGE HOME™

616   784
891   884
241   681
337   987
854   254
994   **774**
824   321

On a mission to save Earth from another alien probe, Kirk and his volunteer crew travel back in time in an old Klingon cruiser to retrieve two humpback whales, and return them to the future. During their travels, they are forced to assimilate into the lifestyle of 1986 San Francisco.

After the perilous journey, the crew are rewarded with the recently commissioned *U.S.S. Enterprise*™ NCC-1701-A, prompting Kirk to declare that they all have come home. ■

784
884
681
987
254
77453284   **774**
66224482   321

OCTOBER					1996			NOVEMBER					1996			DECEMBER					1996	
M	T	W	T	F	S	S		M	T	W	T	F	S	S		M	T	W	T	F	S	S
	1	2	3	4	5	6						1	2	3		30	31					1
7	8	9	10	11	12	13		4	5	6	7	8	9	10		2	3	4	5	6	7	8
14	15	16	17	18	19	20		11	12	13	14	15	16	17		9	10	11	12	13	14	15
21	22	23	24	25	26	27		18	19	20	21	22	23	24		16	17	18	19	20	21	22
28	29	30	31					25	26	27	28	29	30			23	24	25	26	27	28	29

◀ OCTOBER-NOVEMBER ▶

Holiday (Republic of Ireland)
Labour Day (New Zealand)

MONDAY 28

TUESDAY 29

WEDNESDAY 30

Halloween

THURSDAY 31

Captain Kirk commandeers a Klingon Bird-Of-Prey

FRIDAY 1

SATURDAY 2

Culture Day (Japan)

SUNDAY 3

STAR TREK® V: THE FINAL FRONTIER™

616 784
891 884
241 681
337 987
854 254
994 **774**
824 321

In the search for the ultimate secret of life, Spock's half-brother Sybok forces Captain Kirk and his crew into a dangerous journey of self-discovery.

This film was particularly special because it marked the feature film directorial debut of William Shatner. Shatner made strong use of location shooting, providing a welcome change from the Paramount sound stages. ■

616 784
891 884
241 681
337 987
854 254
77453284 994 **774**
66224482 824 321

OCTOBER						1996	NOVEMBER						1996	DECEMBER						1996
M	T	W	T	F	S	S	M	T	W	T	F	S	S	M	T	W	T	F	S	S
	1	2	3	4	5	6					1	2	3	30	31					1
7	8	9	10	11	12	13	4	5	6	7	8	9	10	2	3	4	5	6	7	8
14	15	16	17	18	19	20	11	12	13	14	15	16	17	9	10	11	12	13	14	15
21	22	23	24	25	26	27	18	19	20	21	22	23	24	16	17	18	19	20	21	22
28	29	30	31				25	26	27	28	29	30		23	24	25	26	27	28	29

NOVEMBER

MONDAY 4

TUESDAY 5

WEDNESDAY 6

THURSDAY 7

Robert Duncan McNeill's Birthday (Lieutenant Tom Paris)

FRIDAY 8

SATURDAY 9

Remembrance Sunday (UK)

SUNDAY 10

516 784
891 884
241 681
557 987
254 254
994 **774**
824 321

Spock's protégé, Valeris, is a leading figure amongst a band of disaffected Starfleet officers who do not wish to end the formal hostilities between the Klingon Empire and the Federation.

Using her closeness to Spock and her access to the *U.S.S. Enterprise™*, she delicately executes a plan to sabotage negotiations and maintain the status quo. As a result of this plan, Chancellor Gorkon of the Klingon High Council is assassinated. ■

774
532
84
662
244
82

784
884
681
987
254
774
321

OCTOBER						1996	NOVEMBER						1996	DECEMBER						1996
M	T	W	T	F	S	S	M	T	W	T	F	S	S	M	T	W	T	F	S	S
	1	2	3	4	5	6					1	2	3	30	31					1
7	8	9	10	11	12	13	4	5	6	7	8	9	10	2	3	4	5	6	7	8
14	15	16	17	18	19	20	11	12	13	14	15	16	17	9	10	11	12	13	14	15
21	22	23	24	25	26	27	18	19	20	21	22	23	24	16	17	18	19	20	21	22
28	29	30	31				25	26	27	28	29	30		23	24	25	26	27	28	29

 **NOVEMBER**

Armistice Day (1918) (France)
Veteran's Day (USA)
Remembrance Day (Australia)

MONDAY **11**

TUESDAY **12**

Whoopi Goldberg's Birthday (Guinan)

WEDNESDAY **13**

THURSDAY **14**

FRIDAY **15**

SATURDAY **16**

SUNDAY **17**

STAR TREK® GENERATIONS™

Seen here in space dock is the *U.S.S. Enterprise*™ NCC-1701-B, the last ship to carry Captain Kirk on an adventure. Following a mission to rescue two Federation freighters, Kirk is lost in action.

When Captain Harriman requested Captain Kirk to lead the ship on its maiden voyage, little did he anticipate the gravity of events that would follow. ∎

77453284   774
66224482

OCTOBER						1996		NOVEMBER						1996		DECEMBER						1996
M	T	W	T	F	S	S		M	T	W	T	F	S	S		M	T	W	T	F	S	S
	1	2	3	4	5	6						1	2	3		30	31					1
7	8	9	10	11	12	13		4	5	6	7	8	9	10		2	3	4	5	6	7	8
14	15	16	17	18	19	20		11	12	13	14	15	16	17		9	10	11	12	13	14	15
21	22	23	24	25	26	27		18	19	20	21	22	23	24		16	17	18	19	20	21	22
28	29	30	31					25	26	27	28	29	30			23	24	25	26	27	28	29

NOVEMBER

MONDAY 18

Robert Beltran's Birthday (First Officer Chakotay)

TUESDAY 19

WEDNESDAY 20

Day of Prayer & Repentance (Germany)

Michael Dorn as Lt Cmdr Worf

THURSDAY 21

FRIDAY 22

Labour Thanksgiving (Japan)

SATURDAY 23

Denise Crosby's Birthday (Lt Tasha Yar, Sela)

SUNDAY 24

STAR TREK® ANIMATED

The STAR TREK® animated series was the first new source of STAR TREK adventures on television since the cancellation of the original series in June 1969.

Twenty-two 20-minute episodes were made circa 1973, featuring the voices of the original crew. Several of the actors drew on their experience to create the voices of many of the aliens that appeared in the shows. ■

NOVEMBER						1996
M	T	W	T	F	S	S
				1	2	3
4	5	6	7	8	9	10
11	12	13	14	15	16	17
18	19	20	21	22	23	24
25	26	27	28	29	30	

DECEMBER						1996
M	T	W	T	F	S	S
30	31					1
2	3	4	5	6	7	8
9	10	11	12	13	14	15
16	17	18	19	20	21	22
23	24	25	26	27	28	29

JANUARY						1997
M	T	W	T	F	S	S
		1	2	3	4	5
6	7	8	9	10	11	12
13	14	15	16	17	18	19
20	21	22	23	24	25	26
27	28	29	30	31		

◀ NOVEMBER-DECEMBER ■

MONDAY **25**

TUESDAY **26**

WEDNESDAY **27**

Thanksgiving Day (USA)

THURSDAY **28**

FRIDAY **29**

SATURDAY **30**

SUNDAY **1**

10045

10046

77453284
66224482

10047

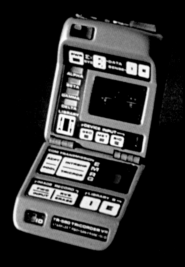

10048

254
774

Some of the wonderful
STAR TREK® technical
devices.

Clockwise from top:
Phaser rifle, Tricorder,
Hand phaser, Isolinear
chips, Medi-kit. ∎

616	784
891	884
241	681
337	987
854	254
994	**774**
824	321

NOVEMBER						1996
M	T	W	T	F	S	S
				1	2	3
4	5	6	7	8	9	10
11	12	13	14	15	16	17
18	19	20	21	22	23	24
25	26	27	28	29	30	

DECEMBER						1996
M	T	W	T	F	S	S
30	31					1
2	3	4	5	6	7	8
9	10	11	12	13	14	15
16	17	18	19	20	21	22
23	24	25	26	27	28	29

JANUARY						1997
M	T	W	T	F	S	S
		1	2	3	4	5
6	7	8	9	10	11	12
13	14	15	16	17	18	19
20	21	22	23	24	25	26
27	28	29	30	31		

◖ DECEMBER ▬

MONDAY **2**

TUESDAY **3**

WEDNESDAY **4**

THURSDAY **5**

Constitution Day (Spain)

FRIDAY **6**

SATURDAY **7**

Immaculate Conception (Spain)

SUNDAY **8**

10045

10046

10047

Above: Patrick Stewart (left) and Michael Piller, executive producer of STAR TREK®: THE NEXT GENERATION™.

Left: William Shatner (left) and David Carson, director of STAR TREK GENERATIONS™.

Below: René Auberjonois with Jonathan Frakes, directing a STAR TREK: DEEP SPACE NINE™ episode. ■

10048

NOVEMBER						1996	DECEMBER						1996	JANUARY						1997
M	T	W	T	F	S	S	M	T	W	T	F	S	S	M	T	W	T	F	S	S
				1	2	3	30	31					1			1	2	3	4	5
4	5	6	7	8	9	10	2	3	4	5	6	7	8	6	7	8	9	10	11	12
11	12	13	14	15	16	17	9	10	11	12	13	14	15	13	14	15	16	17	18	19
18	19	20	21	22	23	24	16	17	18	19	20	21	22	20	21	22	23	24	25	26
25	26	27	28	29	30		23	24	25	26	27	28	29	27	28	29	30	31		

◖ DECEMBER ▬▬

Michael Dorn's Birthday (Lieutenant Commander Worf)

MONDAY 9

TUESDAY 10

WEDNESDAY 11

THURSDAY 12

Garrett Wang's Birthday (Ensign Harry Kim)

FRIDAY 13

SATURDAY 14

SUNDAY 15

616 784
891 884
241 681
337 987
854 254
994 **774**
824 321

Academy Award® winner Michael Westmore, a master at work, above, with one of the barbers of the *U.S.S. Enterprise*™.

616 **891** 884 681
241 337 987 254
854 994 **774** 321
824 784

    Below with Brent Spiner in his daily extensive transformation into Data, the android. Data's gold make-up takes several hours to apply and he also has to wear yellow contact lenses. ∎

784
884
681
987
254
77453284   **774**
66224482   321

NOVEMBER						1996		DECEMBER						1996		JANUARY						1997
M	T	W	T	F	S	S		M	T	W	T	F	S	S		M	T	W	T	F	S	S
				1	2	3		30	31					1				1	2	3	4	5
4	5	6	7	8	9	10		2	3	4	5	6	7	8		6	7	8	9	10	11	12
11	12	13	14	15	16	17		9	10	11	12	13	14	15		13	14	15	16	17	18	19
18	19	20	21	22	23	24		16	17	18	19	20	21	22		20	21	22	23	24	25	26
25	26	27	28	29	30			23	24	25	26	27	28	29		27	28	29	30	31		

DECEMBER

MONDAY 16

TUESDAY 17

Gwynyth Walsh as one of the Duras sisters, B'Etor

WEDNESDAY 18

THURSDAY 19

FRIDAY 20

SATURDAY 21

SUNDAY 22

616 784
891 884
241 681
337 987
854 254
994 **774**
824 321

Above: The bridge of the *Defiant,* a much more compact area than that on the *U.S.S. Enterprise*™, but just as functional.
Below: 10-Forward, the bar on the *U.S.S. Enterprise*™, where the crew gather to socialise and drink Synthehol. Synthehol is a non-alcoholic drink which tastes like alcohol, without the complication of a hangover the next day! ■

77453284
66224482

616 784
891 884
241 681
337 987
854 254
994 **774**
824 321

NOVEMBER						1996	DECEMBER						1996	JANUARY						1997
M	T	W	T	F	S	S	M	T	W	T	F	S	S	M	T	W	T	F	S	S
				1	2	3	30	31					1			1	2	3	4	5
4	5	6	7	8	9	10	2	3	4	5	6	7	8	6	7	8	9	10	11	12
11	12	13	14	15	16	17	9	10	11	12	13	14	15	13	14	15	16	17	18	19
18	19	20	21	22	23	24	16	17	18	19	20	21	22	20	21	22	23	24	25	26
25	26	27	28	29	30		23	24	25	26	27	28	29	27	28	29	30	31		

 **◖ DECEMBER ▬▬**

Emperor's Birthday (Japan)

MONDAY 23

TUESDAY 24

Rick Berman's Birthday (Executive Producer, ST:TNG, ST:DS9, ST:VOY; Co-Creator ST:DS9, ST:VOY; Producer STAR TREK® GENERATIONS™)

Christmas Day

WEDNESDAY 25

St Stephano Day (Italy)
Boxing Day
Bank Holiday (Scotland)
St Stephen's Day (Republic of Ireland)

THURSDAY 26

FRIDAY 27

Nichelle Nichols' Birthday (Lieutenant Uhura)

SATURDAY 28

SUNDAY 29

THE GREAT BIRD OF THE GALAXY

Below: Gene Roddenberry, creator of STAR TREK®, and his wife Majel Barrett.

The STAR TREK phenomenon, now celebrating four successful television shows over four decades, still carries Roddenberry's optimistic vision of the future. ■

NOVEMBER						1996
M	T	W	T	F	S	S
				1	2	3
4	5	6	7	8	9	10
11	12	13	14	15	16	17
18	19	20	21	22	23	24
25	26	27	28	29	30	

DECEMBER						1996
M	T	W	T	F	S	S
30	31					1
2	3	4	5	6	7	8
9	10	11	12	13	14	15
16	17	18	19	20	21	22
23	24	25	26	27	28	29

JANUARY						1997
M	T	W	T	F	S	S
		1	2	3	4	5
6	7	8	9	10	11	12
13	14	15	16	17	18	19
20	21	22	23	24	25	26
27	28	29	30	31		

DECEMBER-JANUARY

MONDAY 30

TUESDAY 31

New Year's Day

WEDNESDAY 1

Bank Holiday (Scotland)
New Year's Holiday (New Zealand)

THURSDAY 2

FRIDAY 3

SATURDAY 4

SUNDAY 5

OFFICIAL LOG ►

NAME _____

ADDRESS _____
_____
_____
_____

PH. NO. _____

OFFICIAL LOG ►

NAME _____

ADDRESS _____
_____
_____
_____

PH. NO. _____

OFFICIAL LOG ►

NAME _____

ADDRESS _____
_____
_____
_____

PH. NO. _____

OFFICIAL LOG ►

NAME _____

ADDRESS _____
_____
_____
_____

PH. NO. _____

OFFICIAL LOG ►

NAME _____

ADDRESS _____
_____
_____
_____

PH. NO. _____

OFFICIAL LOG ►

NAME _____

ADDRESS _____
_____
_____
_____

PH. NO. _____

OFFICIAL LOG ►

NAME _____

ADDRESS _____
_____
_____
_____

PH. NO. _____

OFFICIAL LOG ►

NAME _____

ADDRESS _____
_____
_____
_____

PH. NO. _____

OFFICIAL LOG ►

NAME _____

ADDRESS _____
_____
_____
_____

PH. NO. _____

OFFICIAL LOG ►

NAME _____

ADDRESS _____
_____
_____
_____

PH. NO. _____

OFFICIAL LOG ►

NAME _____

ADDRESS _____
_____
_____

PH. NO. _____

OFFICIAL LOG ►

NAME _____

ADDRESS _____
_____
_____

PH. NO. _____

OFFICIAL LOG ►

NAME _____
ADDRESS _____
_____
_____
PH. NO. _____

OFFICIAL LOG ►

NAME _____
ADDRESS _____
_____
_____
PH. NO. _____

OFFICIAL LOG ►

NAME _____
ADDRESS _____
_____
_____
PH. NO. _____

OFFICIAL LOG ►

NAME _____
ADDRESS _____
_____
_____
PH. NO. _____

OFFICIAL LOG ►

NAME _____
ADDRESS _____
_____
_____
PH. NO. _____

OFFICIAL LOG ►

NAME _____
ADDRESS _____
_____
_____
PH. NO. _____

OFFICIAL LOG ►

NAME _____
ADDRESS _____
_____
_____
PH. NO. _____

OFFICIAL LOG ►

NAME _____
ADDRESS _____
_____
_____
PH. NO. _____

OFFICIAL LOG ►

NAME _____
ADDRESS _____
_____
_____
PH. NO. _____

OFFICIAL LOG ►

NAME _____
ADDRESS _____
_____
_____
PH. NO. _____

OFFICIAL LOG ►

NAME _____
ADDRESS _____
_____
_____
PH. NO. _____

OFFICIAL LOG ►

NAME _____
ADDRESS _____
_____
_____
PH. NO. _____

OFFICIAL LOG ▶

NAME _____
ADDRESS _____
_____
_____
PH. NO. _____

OFFICIAL LOG ▶

NAME _____
ADDRESS _____
_____
_____
PH. NO. _____

OFFICIAL LOG ▶

NAME _____
ADDRESS _____
_____
_____
PH. NO. _____

OFFICIAL LOG ▶

NAME _____
ADDRESS _____
_____
_____
PH. NO. _____

OFFICIAL LOG ▶

NAME _____
ADDRESS _____
_____
_____
PH. NO. _____

OFFICIAL LOG ▶

NAME _____
ADDRESS _____
_____
_____
PH. NO. _____

OFFICIAL LOG ▶

NAME _____
ADDRESS _____
_____
_____
PH. NO. _____

OFFICIAL LOG ▶

NAME _____
ADDRESS _____
_____
_____
PH. NO. _____

OFFICIAL LOG ▶

NAME _____
ADDRESS _____
_____
_____
PH. NO. _____

OFFICIAL LOG ▶

NAME _____
ADDRESS _____
_____
_____
PH. NO. _____

OFFICIAL LOG ▶

NAME _____
ADDRESS _____
_____
_____
PH. NO. _____

OFFICIAL LOG ▶

NAME _____
ADDRESS _____
_____
_____
PH. NO. _____

OFFICIAL LOG ▶

NAME _____
ADDRESS _____
_____
_____
PH. NO. _____

OFFICIAL LOG ▶

NAME _____
ADDRESS _____
_____
_____
PH. NO. _____

OFFICIAL LOG ▶

NAME _____
ADDRESS _____
_____
_____
PH. NO. _____

OFFICIAL LOG ▶

NAME _____
ADDRESS _____
_____
_____
PH. NO. _____

OFFICIAL LOG ▶

NAME _____
ADDRESS _____
_____
_____
PH. NO. _____

OFFICIAL LOG ▶

NAME _____
ADDRESS _____
_____
_____
PH. NO. _____

OFFICIAL LOG ▶

NAME _____
ADDRESS _____
_____
_____
PH. NO. _____

OFFICIAL LOG ▶

NAME _____
ADDRESS _____
_____
_____
PH. NO. _____

OFFICIAL LOG ▶

NAME _____
ADDRESS _____
_____
_____
PH. NO. _____

OFFICIAL LOG ▶

NAME _____
ADDRESS _____
_____
_____
PH. NO. _____

OFFICIAL LOG ▶

NAME _____
ADDRESS _____
_____
_____
PH. NO. _____

OFFICIAL LOG ▶

NAME _____
ADDRESS _____
_____
_____
PH. NO. _____

THE STAR® TREK DIARY 1996

Designed and edited by George Papadeas

First published in Australasia in 1995 by
Simon & Schuster Australia
20 Barcoo Street
East Roseville NSW 2069

First published in Great Britain in 1995 by
Simon & Schuster Limited
West Garden Place, Kendal Street
London W2 2AQ

Viacom International
Sydney New York London Toronto Tokyo Singapore

ISBN: 0 671 85515 8

Produced in Hong Kong by Mandarin Offset

The Publishers would like to thank Maria Papadeas and the staff at Stratagem
for their invaluable assistance in putting this diary together.